Donkey and Monkey

by John Shefelbine
Illustrated by Sheila Lucas

SCHOLASTIC

Donkey and Monkey were
friends. They lived by a big lake
with a sandy shore. Two trees hid
them from the hot sun.

One day Monkey's father came
to visit. They all sat in the shade
and had some mint tea. Then they
went for a walk along the lake.

Monkey's father told some jokes.

His jokes were funny. Monkey and

Donkey were happy.

All of a sudden, Monkey said,
"Look! I see a little box in the
sand." He ran and picked it up.

Donkey said, "We need a key.
Maybe the key is in the sand." So
they all looked for the key.

"I see it," said Monkey's father.

He picked up a rusty little key

and put it in the keyhole.

It unlocked the box.

What was inside? A map!

"What do you think we will find
if we follow it?" asked Donkey.

Seek and look
Here and there.
Follow this map
To show you where.

Stand in front of the tree.
Look at the lake.
Then take ten steps.

Now go around the big rock,

where you will see two bushes.

Go six big steps past them.

Is a low rock wall next to you?

Jump up on this wall,

but don't fall!

Do you see two paths?
Follow the path on the left
all the way to the end.

Now look for a low, flat rock.

It is between a big and a little tree.

Look in the deep grass next to the rock.

Donkey and Monkey dashed to
the rock. They looked in the tall
grass. "I see it," said Donkey.
"It's a jar. It says HONEY!"

Monkey's father smiled. Then they all sat down and had some tea and honey.

Who put the map in the box and the honey in the grass?

My Words

*along
*front

ey

Donkey
honey
key
Monkey
Monkey's

Story Words: jar

*new high frequency words

ISBN 0-590-99930-3   Copyright © 1997 by Scholastic Inc.   All rights reserved.   Printed in the U.S.A.